The Organist's Companion
From Lent to Easter

The Organist's Companion From Lent to Easter

Over 50 seasonal pieces for **Organ**

Kevin Mayhew

We hope you enjoy the music in this book.
Further copies of this and our many other books are available
from your local music shop or Christian bookshop.

In case of difficulty, please contact the publisher direct by writing to:

The Sales Department
KEVIN MAYHEW LTD
Buxhall
Stowmarket
Suffolk IP14 3BW

Phone 01449 737978
Fax 01449 737834
E-mail info@kevinmayhewltd.com

Please ask for our complete catalogue of outstanding Church Music.

First published in Great Britain in 2000 by Kevin Mayhew Ltd.

ISBN 1 84003 673 7
ISMN M 57004 809 0
Catalogue No: 1400271

0 1 2 3 4 5 6 7 8 9

Cover design: Jonathan Stroulger
Music editor and setter: Rob Danter
Proof reader: Marian Hellen

Printed and bound in Malta by Interprint Limited

Contents

About the Composers

Rosalie Bonighton (*b.*1946) is a recitalist, teacher and composer with a special interest in writing music for new liturgical needs.

Andrew Fletcher (*b.*1950) is a teacher, composer, accompanist and recitalist, performing regularly all over the world.

Michael Higgins (*b.*1981) is currently studying music at the Birmingham Conservatoire and is Organ Scholar at St Alban and St Patrick Parish Church, Birmingham.

Elizabeth Hill is a primary school teacher and Organist at St Andrew's Church, Billingborough.

Robert Jones (*b.*1945) has written choral pieces specifically for local schools and churches. Organ music also features largely in his output. Having taught for over 30 years, he is now retired and continues to be an active organist and accompanist.

Richard Lloyd (*b.*1933) was formerly Assistant Organist of Salisbury Cathedral and successively Organist of Hereford and Durham Cathedrals. He now divides his time between examining and composing.

John Marsh (*b.*1939) is a former Organist and Director of Music at St Mary Redcliffe Church, and is now a member of the music staff at Clifton College, Bristol.

Colin Mawby (*b.*1936) was previously Choral Director at Radio Telefís Éireann, the national broadcasting authority in the Republic of Ireland, and Master of the Music at Westminster Cathedral. He is Conductor of Ireland's only full-time professional choir, the National Chamber Choir of Ireland.

Andrew Moore (*b.*1954) is parish priest of Lambourn and Hungerford.

June Nixon is Organist and Director of the Choir at St Paul's Cathedral, Melbourne, Australia. She also teaches at the Melbourne University School of Music.

Richard Pantcheff (*b.*1959) is an organist and composer currently working in Oxford. Many of his works are written for the Episcopal Church of Christ the King, Frankfurt, Germany, as Composer in Association.

Betty Roe (*b.*1930) studied at the Royal Academy of Music and later with Lennox Berkeley. She composes in many forms from solo songs to operas.

David Terry (*b.*1975) studied at Lincoln College, Oxford, where he was Organ Scholar. He is currently sub-organist at Wells Cathedral and on the music staff of Downside School.

Stanley Vann (*b.*1910) was successively Organist at Chelmsford and Peterborough Cathedrals.

Norman Warren (*b.*1934) is Archdeacon of Rochester. He is well known as a composer of hymns, and was a member of the music committee for 'Hymns for Today's Church'.

Andrew Wright was a former Assistant Master of Music at Westminster Cathedral where he also taught music in the Cathedral Choir School. Currently Master of Music and Director of Liturgical Music for the Diocese of Brentwood, his compositions include motets, carols, psalms, mass settings, Gospel Acclamations and, more recently, organ music for the liturgy.

LUX EOI

Norman Warren

ST CHRISTOPHER

Andrew Fletcher

Poco mosso e poco articulato (♩ = c. 52)

BRESLAU

Michael Higgins

O FILII ET FILIAE

Richard Lloyd

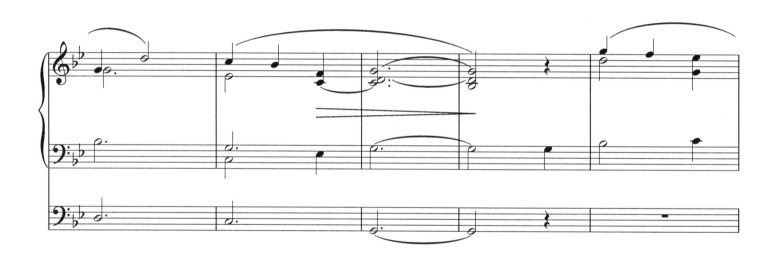

For Gareth Williams and the historic Gray and Davison organ at St Mary's, Usk

ELLACOMBE

Robert Jones

For Puffin

REGENT SQUARE

Betty Roe

ABRIDGE

Rosalie Bonighton

THIS JOYFUL EASTERTIDE

Andrew Wright

25

ROCKINGHAM

Elizabeth Hill

SONG 13

Richard Pantcheff

HOLY JESU

John Marsh

Andante cantabile

33

MISERICORDIA

Andrew Moore

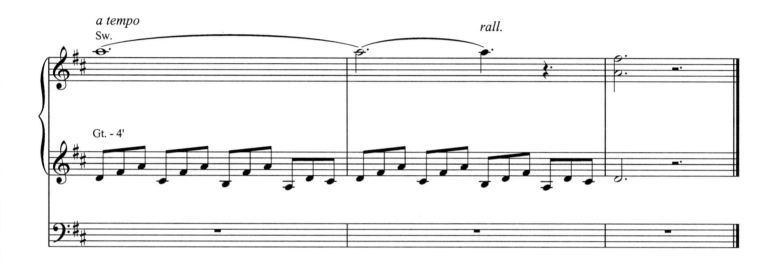

ST ALBINUS

June Nixon

37

NOEL NOUVELET

Stanley Vann

40

rall. moltissimo

WÜRTTEMBERG

Richard Lloyd

BISHOPTHORPE

Colin Mawby

47

HORSLEY

David Terry

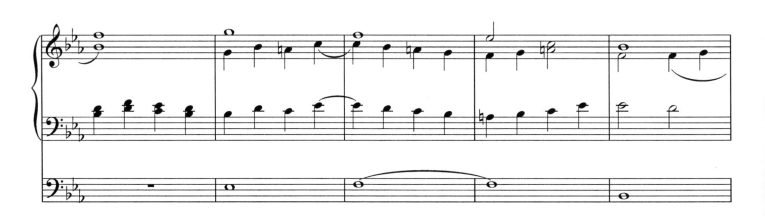

HYFRYDOL

Andrew Wright

Risoluto (♩ = 138)

Gt. + Sw. *f*

Gt. + Sw. to Ped.

For Puffin

ST FRANCIS XAVIER

Betty Roe

SAVANNAH

Rosalie Bonighton

ST THOMAS (WEBBE)

Robert Jones

PASSION CHORALE

Richard Lloyd

DEUS TUORUM MILITUM

Andrew Fletcher

allargando

SOUTHWELL (DAMON)

June Nixon

PETRA (REDHEAD NO. 76)

Michael Higgins

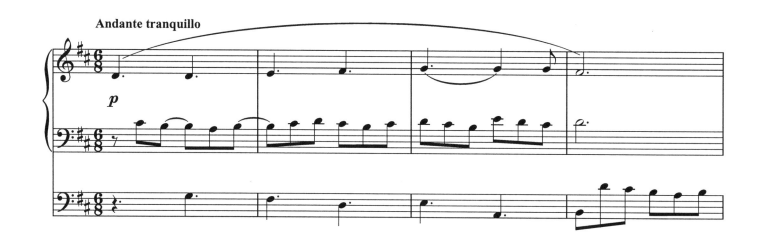

For Dominic

MACCABAEUS

David Terry

SALZBURG

Rosalie Bonighton

ST THEODULPH

Norman Warren

HERONGATE

Andrew Moore

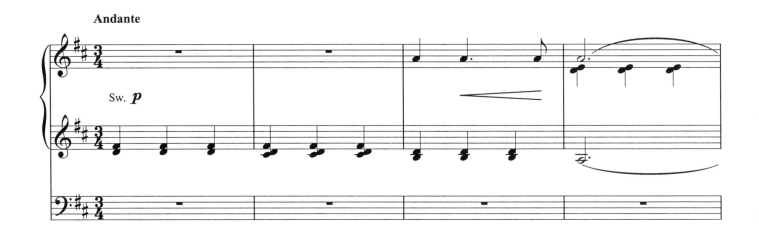

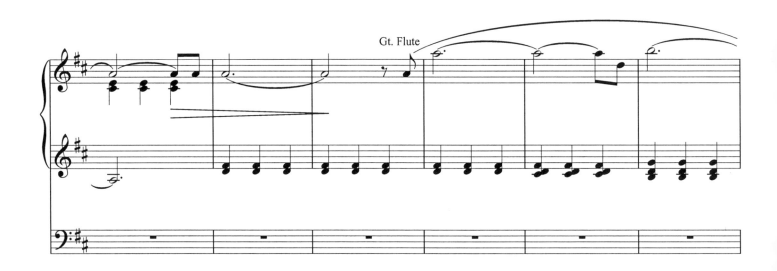

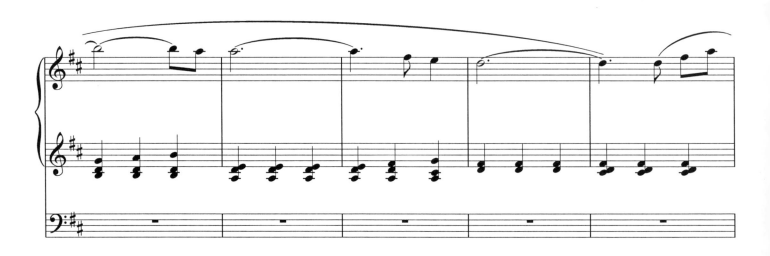

ST JOHN DAMASCENE

John Marsh

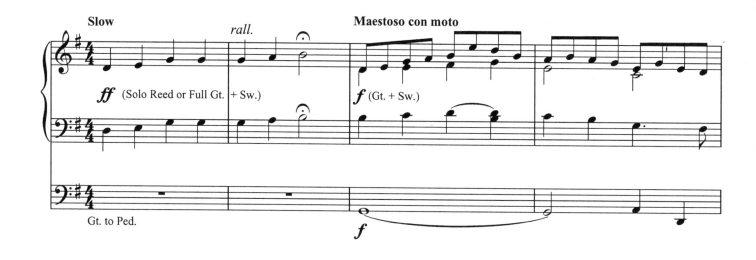

rall.

Largamente   **Slow**

I NEED THEE

Colin Mawby

CASWALL

Richard Lloyd

ST BERNARD

Andrew Wright

poco rit.

91

STABAT MATER

Rosalie Bonighton

93

ST FULBERT

Norman Warren

poco rall. al fine

96

WINCHESTER NEW

Stanley Vann

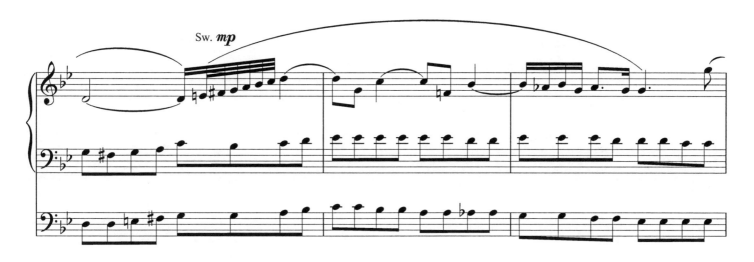

For Ieuan Davies

DONCASTER

Robert Jones

SONG 46

Richard Lloyd

poco a poco meno mosso

GELOB'T SEI GOTT (VULPIUS)

Colin Mawby

For Puffin

CLOISTERS

Betty Roe

OLIVET

June Nixon

EASTER HYMN

Andrew Moore

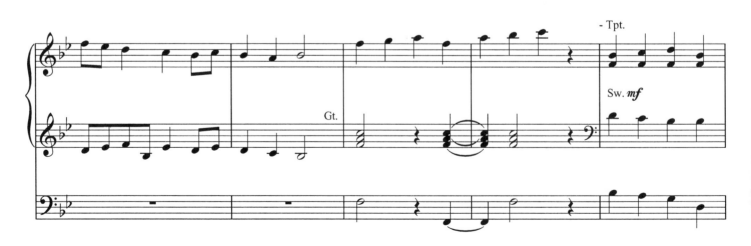

HERZLIEBSTER JESU

Elizabeth Hill

ST HUGH

Rosalie Bonighton

NARENZA

David Terry

WYCHBOLD

Richard Pantcheff

GERONTIUS

Stanley Vann

REPTON

Andrew Fletcher

Poco andante (♩ = 66)

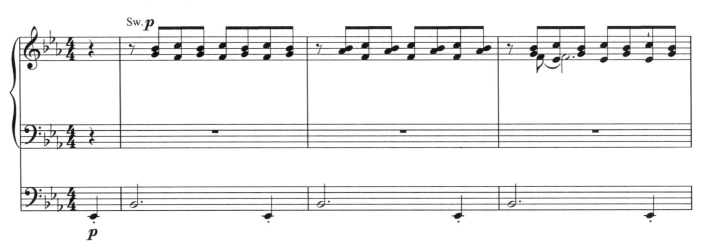

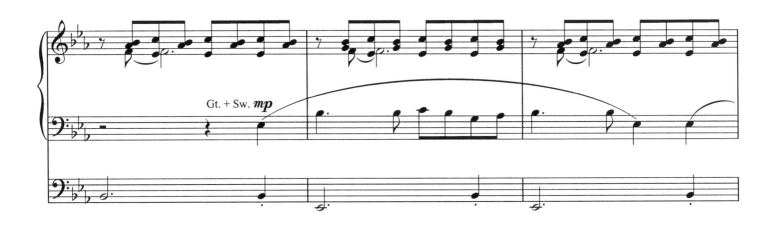

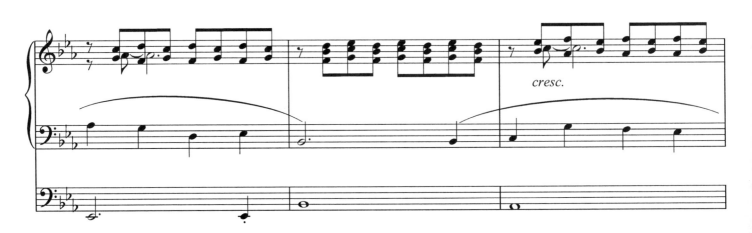

ANIMA CHRISTI

Michael Higgins

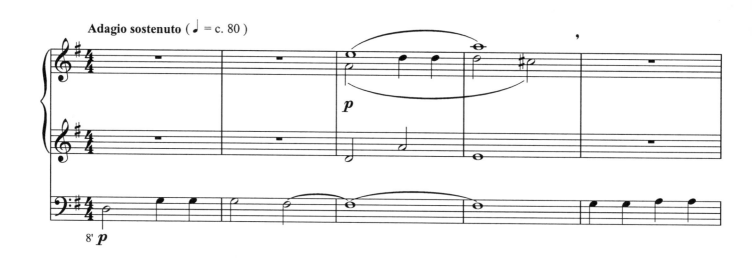

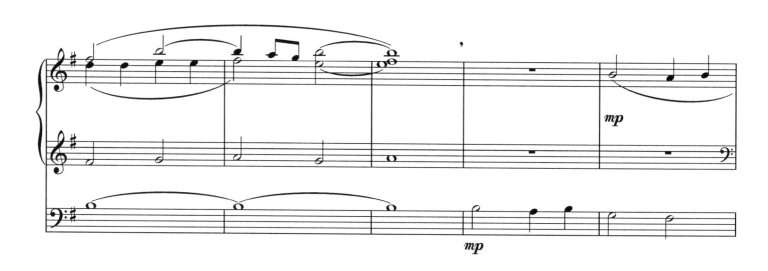

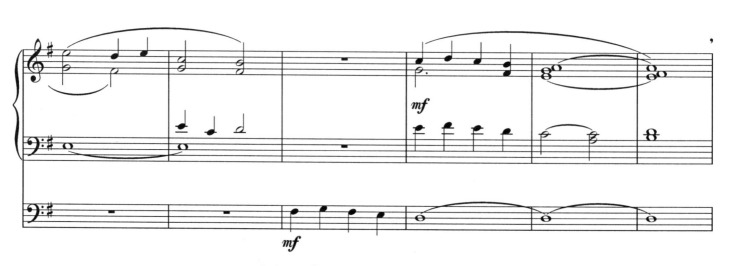

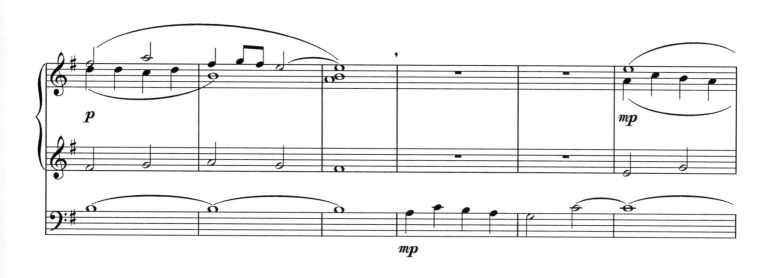

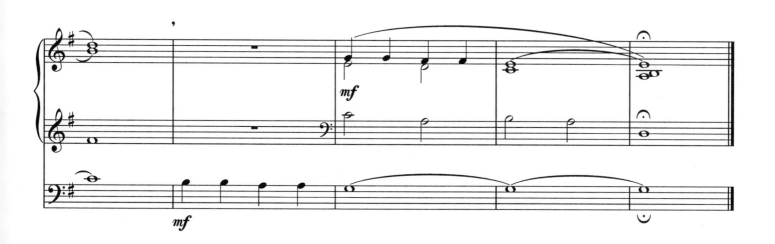

AUS DER TIEFE

John Marsh

NEANDER

Richard Lloyd

Con brio ma un poco maestoso

135

ALBANO

Rosalie Bonighton

CHURCH TRIUMPHANT

Richard Pantcheff

142